21·50
.36 for 2

exploring your emotions

Instruction Manual

by
Angela Holland
Alison Payne
Lindsey Vickery

Acknowledgements

We would like to thank all of the people featured in the photographs and for giving their consent for the publication of the material. In particular, we would like to express our sincere gratitude to Melton Mowbray College of Further Education, Leicestershire and their drama students for all their help and also to Mr Payne for his time in taking most of the photographs.

Contents

Introduction

Purpose of this Pack

The Exploring Your Emotions pack is designed to be a versatile set of photographs for use with adults with learning disabilities and for people with other disabilities. The photographs show people demonstrating an emotional state or in a situation likely to evoke an emotional response e.g. returning home after a time away. They can be used in a variety of ways:

- In a therapeutic capacity to enable adults with learning disabilities to explore, express and develop emotional understanding in relation to their life experiences.

- To support people to develop a language for their emotions. The pack can help people understand and talk about some ways in which people respond to emotive and distressing situations.

- As a tool in establishing and developing a therapeutic relationship. The pack can be used to help individuals to talk about emotions in a safe and non-threatening manner by reference to the people and situations shown in the photographs. Individuals who have limited linguistic abilities or are reluctant to rely upon the spoken word may prefer to draw their responses to the photographs.

The pack is not intended to be used as a 'quick answer' to major distress for people with disabilities. Some people will need long-term supportive work to address their personal distress, and it is hoped that these materials will be used to support this.

Why Photographs?

Images often trigger memories, allowing a person to remember and progress towards expressing feelings associated with past experiences. Initially, it can be less threatening to comment upon other people's experiences rather than your own.

The photographs show people in a range of settings and expressing different emotions. It is helpful to plan in advance which photographs are likely to be helpful in working with an individual person. For example, it might be appropriate to begin by exploring how well a person is able to describe emotions on the basis of facial expression, before moving on to talk about emotions which occur in response to different kinds of experience. The photographs are designed to help people explore a range of common emotions together with experiences which may have involved strong emotional reactions.

Who can use the Exploring Your Emotions Pack?

The pack is intended for use by professionals working with adults with learning disabilities, such as clinical psychologists, psychiatrists, community nurses, day centre officers, social workers, speech and language therapists and occupational therapists. It is recommended that the professionals need to have experience in working with people who may be distressed, and that appropriate personal supervision is available.

It is important to be aware that the photographs cover some sensitive issues and may allow previously hidden feelings to come to the surface, and for this reason, we suggest the pack is always used under the supervision of an experienced and appropriately qualified professional.

Background

What are Emotions?

Early theories of emotion emphasised the link between emotions and physiological responses. When we experience an intense emotion (such as fear or anger) we are aware of bodily changes - rapid heart beat and breathing, dry mouth, increased muscle tension, perspiration, trembling and a 'sinking feeling' in the stomach. Most of these physiological changes result from the activation of the sympathetic division of the autonomic nervous system, as it prepares the body for emergency action. One of the earliest theories of emotion proposed that the perception of the physiological changes *is* the emotion. William James at Harvard in the late 1800's believed that the important factor in our felt emotion is the feedback from the bodily changes that occur in response to a frightening or upsetting situation. For example, he stated "we are afraid because we can run". A Danish researcher, Carl Lange, put forward a similar proposal at about the same time, and the theory became known as the James-Lange theory.

The major objections to the James-Lange theory came from Walter Cannon, a physiologist at the University of Chicago. Cannon pointed out that bodily changes do not differ very much from one emotional state to another, despite the fact that people are usually clear about which emotions we are experiencing. Internal organs are relatively insensitive structures not well supplied with nerves, and internal changes occur relatively slowly and are unlikely to be a source of emotion. Cannon assigned a major role in emotion to a structure in the brain called the thalamus. He suggested that the thalamus responded to an emotion-producing stimulus by sending impulses *simultaneously* to the cerebral cortex and to other parts of the body; emotional feelings were the result of joint arousal of the cortex and the sympathetic nervous system. According to this view, the bodily changes and the experience of emotion occur at the same time (Cannon 1927). Subsequent research showed that it is the hypothalamus, rather than the thalamus, which is the important area of the brain for the integration of emotional impulses.

More recently, theories have emphasised the *cognitive* factors in emotion. The individual's appraisal of the emotion-producing situation is an important factor in determining the emotional response. Schachter and Singer (1962) proposed that emotional states are a function of the interaction of cognitive factors and a state of physiological arousal. Feedback to the brain from physiological activity gives rise to an undifferentiated state of affect; but the felt emotion is determined by the 'label' the person assigns to that aroused state. The assignment of a label is a cognitive process; people use information from their past experiences and perceptions of what is happening around them to arrive at an interpretation of the feelings. This interpretation will determine how we act and the label used to define the emotional state. For example, hearing a sound in the middle of the night will give rise to *fear* if it is appraised as the sound of a burglar; it might give rise to *relief*, if it is appraised as your teenage daughter returning late from a party. The *appraisal* determines the emotional response.

Frijda (1986) suggested that emotion comprises of four elements:
- a particular affect or feeling to which we give labels, for example, happy, sad, angry
- a physiological arousal resulting in bodily changes
- a cognitive appraisal or interpretation of a situation
- a behavioural reaction as a direct expression of an emotion

However, the nature of the relationship between affect and cognition is now considered to be more complex than the original cognitive theories acknowledged.

In the early cognitive models of emotional responding, it was believed that the cognitive process of appraisal determined the nature of the emotional response in a simple linear relationship. This rather simplistic model has been questioned, and there is now a growing understanding that some forms of emotional experience are processed directly without any conscious appraisal process intervening. This theoretical shift has important implications. Firstly, it allows a more significant and powerful role to emotion than in the early cognitive theories. Secondly, it opens the door to the incorporation of *unconscious* processes into the theoretical explanations of emotional disorders. The Interacting Cognitive Systems model, or ICS, is a recent example of a theoretical framework in which such ideas have been developed (Barnard and Teasdale 1991). The basic assumption in the ICS model is that mental activity reflects the collective action of several specific processes, each with a particular function to perform. This produces a dynamically interacting system with a range of subsystems. Cognitive processing depends upon the interactions between different subsystems, each of which is specialised in the way it handles specific information. For example, the acoustic sub-system encodes dimensions such as sound frequency, intensity; the body state subsystem encodes information in relation to bodily sensations of pressure, pain etc.

In the ICS model, emotion is the result of system wide activity. Each of the different subsystems can contribute, directly or indirectly, to the experience of emotion. An important distinction is drawn between different forms of knowledge which reflect the operation of different subsystems. This explains why a person can recognise ideas at an intellectual level, but not at an emotional level. For example, a person who believes that he is worthless, or undeserving, may know that he has done a job well, that he has friends, but such facts do not shake the emotional strength of the belief. It is quite possible to know of something 'with the head' but to have a different sense of knowing 'with the heart'. The ICS model is a helpful advance in cognitive theory particularly in the way it recognises the complexity of emotions. The model encompasses the experience of emotions whose origins are, at least in part, *unconscious.* There is a striking parallel with psychodynamic theories of emotional responding.

Goleman (1996) argues that our emotions have a greater impact on our quality of life than was previously recognised. He suggests that our view of human intelligence is far too narrow, and that emotions play a major role in thought, decision-making and individual success. Goleman uses the term 'emotional intelligence' to describe the qualities that help people to succeed in their personal relationships and to develop characteristics of self-discipline, and compassion. He demonstrates that the costs of having a poor understanding of our emotions can range from problems in marriage and parenting, to poor physical and mental health, and a higher potential for physical violence. Goleman argues that emotional intelligence can be strengthened in all of us. He suggests that an effective program would help people to increase a range of emotional skills, for example, identifying and labelling feelings, expressing feelings, managing feelings. Greenberg (1992) has demonstrated that the approach can be helpful for special needs students and can influence classroom behaviour.

Emotions and People with Disabilities

The area of emotional understanding is relatively under-researched in relation to adults with learning disabilities. There are very few assessment and therapeutic materials available to help people to explore this fundamental area.

The limited research to date has suggested that:

- Individuals with learning disabilities have difficulty in interpreting emotions.

- Gray et al (1983) found the overall performance with photographs showing expressions of basic emotions correlated with the intellectual ability and language comprehension of the subject.

- Fear and anger are poorly recognised and are frequently confused with other emotions such as disgust and surprise in individuals with a learning disability.

- Rejecting emotions are poorly interpreted, with individuals tending to dismiss them entirely or confuse them. It is unclear whether this is linked with the individual's verbal abilities. In addition, Stokes (1987) has highlighted the importance of powerful unconscious memories and the subsequent effect on one's ability to remember emotional events.

The Exploring Your Emotions pack is designed to raise the profile of emotions among people with disabilities. Services have traditionally emphasised a practical skills building model of intervention, and clearly this has improved the quality of life of many people. However, it is equally important to address the emotional world of a person with a disability, and the impact that this may have on an individual's overall sense of well being.

References

Barnard, P. J. and Teasdale, J. D. (1991) Interacting Cognitive Subsystems: A systematic approach to cognitive-affective interaction and change. *Cognition and Emotion,* 5, 1-39

Cannon, W. B. (1927) The James-Lange theory of emotion: A critical examination and an alternative theory. *American Journal of Psychology,* 39, 106-124

Frijda, N. (1986) *The Emotions.* Cambridge: Cambridge University Press

Greenberg, M. (1992) Fast Track Project. University of Washington. Conduct Problems Research Group. A Developmental and Clinical Model for the Prevention of Conduct Disorder: The Fast Track Program. *Development and Psychopathology,* 4.

Goleman, D. (1996) *Emotional Intelligence. Why it can matter more than I.Q.* London: Bloomsbury Publishing

Gray, J. M., Fraser, W. L. and Leudar, I. (1983) Recognition of emotion from facial expression in mental handicap. *British Journal of Psychiatry,* 142, 566-571

Schachter, S. and Singer, J. E. (1962) Cognitive, social and physiological determinants of emotional state. *Physiological Review,* 69, 379-399

Stokes, J. (1987) *Insights from psychotherapy, paper presented at the International Symposium on Mental Handicap,* Royal Society of Medicine, 25 February, 1992

Contents of the Pack

The Exploring Your Emotions Pack consists of 30 photographs each numbered on the reverse. The photos cover the majority of basic emotions, for example, happy, sad, angry, but more subtle distinctions, for example, shame or disgust are not represented in separate photographs. Clearly, these are relevant to people with disabilities, and could be included in discussions. Some photographs refer to basic social skills such as personal space - the invasion of which can lead to an emotional response. A complete list of photographs is available on page 14.

There are three sections:

- Basic Emotions: happy, sad, angry, fear, surprise, shock. One photograph shows a person looking bored. While boredom is not usually viewed as an emotion, but rather as a state, it was considered relevant to include this aspect of experience.

- Scenarios. This section shows people in a variety of social situations which are likely to elicit emotional responses.

- Emotional Responses. This section contains photographs of the behaviours which are often associated with various emotional responses, for example, hiding, crying, shouting, hitting, two people consoling each other.

The emotional content of some of the photographs can yield alternative responses, for example, photograph number three is intended to show a young woman feeling shocked, but other interpretations are also appropriate, e.g. fear. In reality, many situations are open to different interpretations.

Guidelines for Use

It is essential that the materials are used with care and sensitivity. Practitioners using the pack should be aware that discussing emotional issues can evoke powerful feelings, for example, about past losses or abandonment. It may be that a person does not want to discuss painful issues unless the time and circumstances are right for them. It is important that this is respected and that practitioners are alert to signs that the experience of some emotions may be distressing. When used appropriately, the pack has potential to be useful to people with disabilities and their carers by allowing a discussion of emotional issues.

The materials can be used in two ways:
- as a support to a therapeutic intervention
- for assessment purposes

The pack is intended to be used in a flexible way, and so instructions for use are considered potentially restrictive. The following suggestions are intended as general guidelines.

Introduction of the Photographs

The material in this pack is designed to be responsive to the issues relevant for each individual. The photographs should be introduced with an explanation outlining why the materials are being used, and with a brief outline of what to do, for example:

Sometimes it is easier to look at pictures than to talk. Could we look at this picture?

Some questions are suitable for starting points, for example:

- What is happening in this photograph?
- What is the man/woman doing?
- How is she/he feeling?

Later on in the session(s) questions could be asked which relate to the individual's experience of emotions, for example:

- What do you do when you're feeling (angry, sad, etc..)?
- Where do you feel (happy, sad, etc..)?
- Have you ever felt like that?

It is extremely important to plan the order of photographs so that sensitive issues are addressed in the middle of the session rather than at the end.

Therapy

The materials are appropriate in a range of therapeutic situations:

- in opening up issues for discussion
- to explore the feelings and emotions which may be described
- to support people who find it difficult to use spoken language.

There is no 'ideal' response to the photographs. The practitioner is interested in the response in terms of a person's understanding of emotions, both their own and other people's. It may then be possible to explore emotional distress, and to become 'emotionally available' for the person. In this way, long term psychotherapy may be supported. The materials were originally designed to be used with individuals, but with careful planning they can also be used in some group situations. Photographs can be selected to address issues relevant to each person or group of people, e.g. leaving home.

Assessment

It is emphasised that the pack is not intended to be a test of how well people recognise expressions of emotion and all responses should be regarded as valid. The responses should help practitioners to gain an insight into a person's understanding of emotions.

The photographs may be used for assessment when:

- a person is experiencing difficulty understanding and managing their own emotions.

- a person has difficulty understanding the emotions and responses of others. The development of empathy and understanding a viewpoint other than their own, could be investigated.

- a person, whose emotions are inhibited, demonstrates distress in another way, for example, challenging behaviour or withdrawal.

The information can be used to understand a person's difficulties and could influence therapeutic intervention. It is important to allow a person to have emotions providing this does not result in physical harm to themselves or others.

All the photographs in Section A should be shown and responses recorded.

Section A comprises photographs of: **Basic Emotions**

No. 1 : A woman smiling, feeling happy.
No. 2 : A sad man.
No. 3 : A woman feeling shocked.
No. 4 : A woman feeling frightened.
No. 5 : An angry man.
No. 6 : A man feeling bored.
No. 7 : A woman crying, feeling sad.
No. 8 : A woman feeling surprised.

To gain an insight into more complex emotions and scenarios, a selection of photographs from Section B can also be shown.

Section B comprises photographs of: **Scenarios**

No. 9 : Leaving, saying goodbye to friends.
No. 10 : Welcome home.
No. 11 : Saying goodbye to other people.
No. 12 : People in conversation, one is not interested.
No. 13 : Rejection.

No. 14 : Threatening another person
No. 15 : Invading another person's space.
No. 16 : A person spilling coffee. An accident or a joke?
No. 17 : Relaxing.
No. 18 : Receiving some news.
No. 19 : Graveside scene.
No. 20 : Cancellation.
No. 21 : Birthday party.

The nine photographs in Section C identify different responses to emotional situations, for example, avoidance, discussion with others, anger, sharing of memories.

Section C comprises photographs of: **Emotional Responses**

No. 22 : A person hits the other person. Anger.
No. 23 : Hiding in a corner. Upset and afraid.
No. 24 : People arguing, shouting. Anger.
No. 25 : An angry man.
No. 26 : Walking away. Rejected.
No. 27 : One person consoling another. Sadness.
No. 28 : Looking at a photograph. Reminiscing.
No. 29 : Alone. Calming down. Thinking through things.
No. 30 : Sharing time together. Building bridges - re-establishing a friendship.

Options

The following options provide an idea of the type of photographs which can be chosen to address specific issues.

Option 1

For a client who has recently experienced a bereavement in his/her family, photographs such as:

No. 2 : Man feeling sad.
No. 7 : Woman crying.
No. 19 : Woman putting flowers on a grave.
No. 5 : Man looking angry.
No. 27 : Woman being comforted.
No. 23 : Woman hiding in a corner.
No. 28 : Woman looking at photograph.

The photographs can facilitate a discussion of feelings of loss, abandonment, sadness, and being able eventually to recall past events without overwhelming distress.

Option 2

To address the issue of change in a person's life:

No. 2 : Man feeling sad.
No. 9 : Leaving.
No. 11 : Saying goodbye.
No. 20 : Activity cancelled.
No. 10 : Welcome home.
No. 29 : Woman sitting on stairs.

The photographs can facilitate a discussion of loss, disappointment and sadness, but also a positive feeling of being welcomed.

Exploring Your Emotions

List of Photographs

Basic Emotions - Section A

No. 1 : A woman smiling, feeling happy.
No. 2 : A sad man.
No. 3 : A woman feeling shocked.
No. 4 : A woman feeling frightened.
No. 5 : An angry man.
No. 6 : A man feeling bored.
No. 7 : A woman crying, feeling sad.
No. 8 : A woman feeling surprised.

Scenarios - Section B

No. 9 : Leaving, saying goodbye to friends.
No. 10 : Welcome home.
No. 11 : Saying goodbye to other people.
No. 12 : People in conversation, one is not interested.
No. 13 : Rejection.
No. 14 : Threatening another person.
No. 15 : Invading another person's space.
No. 16 : A person spilling coffee. An accident or a joke?
No. 17 : Relaxing.
No. 18 : Receiving some news.
No. 19 : Graveside scene.
No. 20 : Cancellation.
No. 21 : Birthday party.

Emotional Responses - Section C

No. 22 : A person hits the other person. Anger.
No. 23 : Hiding in a corner. Upset and afraid.
No. 24 : People arguing, shouting. Anger.
No. 25 : An angry man.
No. 26 : Walking away. Rejected.
No. 27 : One person consoling another. Sadness.
No. 28 : Looking at a photograph. Reminiscing.
No. 29 : Alone. Calming down. Thinking through things.
No. 30 : Sharing time together. Building bridges - re-establishing a friendship.